THIS JOURNAL BELONGS TO:

_____

FOR THE RECORD

MY CURRENT PERSONAL BESTS

5K - DATE_____ TIME_____ PACE_____

10K - DATE_____ TIME_____ PACE_____

20K - DATE_____ TIME_____ PACE_____

HALF MARATHON - DATE_____ TIME_____ PACE_____

MARATHON - DATE_____ TIME_____ PACE_____

ULTRAMARATHON - DATE_____ TIME_____
DISTANCE_____ PACE_____

RUNNING LOCATION
BUCKET LIST

- ALTA VIA 1, THE DOLOMITES, ITALY

- LAGUNAS ATLAS LOOP TRAIL, PATAGONIA PARK, CHILE

- RIM-TO-RIM, GRAND CANYON NATIONAL PARK, ARIZONA

- TOUR DU MONT BLANC, SWITZERLAND, ITALY, FRANCE

MY GOALS

RUN _____ KM, IN A TIME OF _____

ENTER: _____ RACE

ACHIEVE A _____ MIN PER KM PACE

RUN FROM: _____ TO: _____

MY INCENTIVE: _____

_____

_____

_____

_____

RUN _____ KM, IN A TIME OF _____

ENTER: _____ RACE

ACHIEVE A _____ MIN PER KM PACE

RUN FROM: _____ TO: _____

MY INCENTIVE: _____

_____

_____

_____

_____

MY GOALS

RUN _____ KM, IN A TIME OF _____

ENTER: _____ RACE

ACHIEVE A _____ MIN PER KM PACE

RUN FROM: _____ TO: _____

MY INCENTIVE: _____

_____

_____

_____

_____

MY GOALS

RUN _____ KM, IN A TIME OF _____

ENTER: _____ RACE

ACHIEVE A _____ MIN PER KM PACE

RUN FROM: _____ TO: _____

MY INCENTIVE: _____

_____

_____

_____

_____

MY GOALS

RUN _____ KM, IN A TIME OF _____

ENTER: _____ RACE

ACHIEVE A _____ MIN PER KM PACE

RUN FROM: _____ TO: _____

MY INCENTIVE: _____

_____

_____

_____

_____

RUN _____ KM, IN A TIME OF _____

ENTER: _____ RACE

ACHIEVE A _____ MIN PER KM PACE

RUN FROM: _____ TO: _____

MY INCENTIVE: _____

_____

_____

_____

_____

MY GOALS

RUN _____ KM, IN A TIME OF _____

ENTER: _____ RACE

ACHIEVE A _____ MIN PER KM PACE

RUN FROM: _____ TO: _____

MY INCENTIVE: _____

_____

_____

_____

_____

RUN _____ KM, IN A TIME OF _____

ENTER: _____ RACE

ACHIEVE A _____ MIN PER KM PACE

RUN FROM: _____ TO: _____

MY INCENTIVE: _____

_____

_____

_____

_____

MY GOALS

RUN _____ KM, IN A TIME OF _____

ENTER: _____ RACE

ACHIEVE A _____ MIN PER KM PACE

RUN FROM: _____ TO: _____

MY INCENTIVE: _____
_____
_____
_____
_____

RUN _____ KM, IN A TIME OF _____

ENTER: _____ RACE

ACHIEVE A _____ MIN PER KM PACE

RUN FROM: _____ TO: _____

MY INCENTIVE: _____
_____
_____
_____
_____

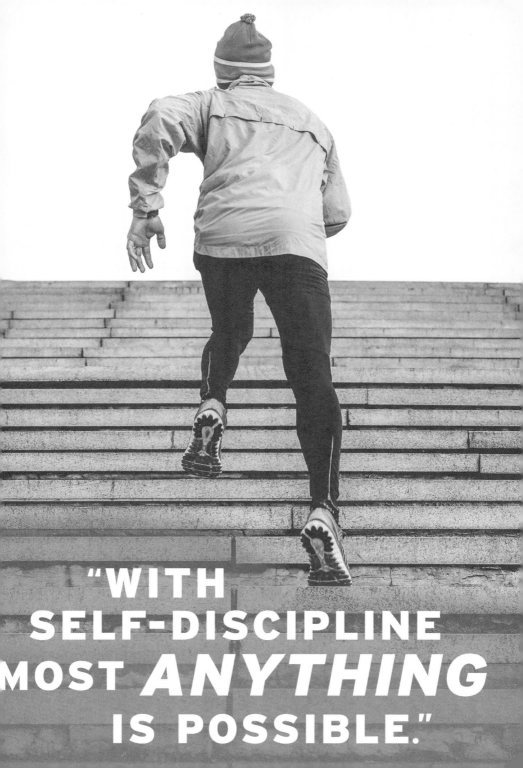

"WITH SELF-DISCIPLINE MOST *ANYTHING* IS POSSIBLE."

CLUBS & ORGANISATIONS

CLUB / ORGANISATION: _____

CONTACT NAME: _____

PHONE: _____

EMAIL / SOCIAL: _____

REGULAR RUNS: _____

DAY:_____TIME: _____MEETING PLACE: _____

CLUB / ORGANISATION: _____

CONTACT NAME: _____

PHONE: _____

EMAIL / SOCIAL: _____

REGULAR RUNS: _____

DAY:_____TIME: _____MEETING PLACE: _____

CLUBS & ORGANISATIONS

CLUB / ORGANISATION: _____

CONTACT NAME: _____

PHONE: _____

EMAIL / SOCIAL: _____

REGULAR RUNS: _____

DAY: _____ TIME: _____ MEETING PLACE: _____

CLUB / ORGANISATION: _____

CONTACT NAME: _____

PHONE: _____

EMAIL / SOCIAL: _____

REGULAR RUNS: _____

DAY: _____ TIME: _____ MEETING PLACE: _____

KEY EVENT RACE DETAILS

EVENT: _____

DATE: _____

LOCATION: _____

ORGANISATION: _____

CONTACT: _____

PHONE: _____

ADDRESS: _____

WEBSITE: _____

EMAIL / SOCIAL: _____

ENTRY CONFIRMED? ☐ YES ☐ NO

RACE NUMBER: _____

START TIME / SIGN ON: _____

RESULT
POSITION: _____ TIME: _____ PACE: _____

KEY EVENT RACE DETAILS

EVENT: _____

DATE: _____

LOCATION: _____

ORGANISATION: _____

CONTACT: _____

PHONE: _____

ADDRESS: _____

WEBSITE: _____

EMAIL / SOCIAL: _____

ENTRY CONFIRMED? ☐ YES ☐ NO

RACE NUMBER: _____

START TIME / SIGN ON: _____

RESULT

POSITION: _____ TIME: _____ PACE: _____

KEY EVENT RACE DETAILS

EVENT: _____

DATE: _____

LOCATION: _____

ORGANISATION: _____

CONTACT: _____

PHONE: _____

ADDRESS: _____

WEBSITE: _____

EMAIL / SOCIAL: _____

ENTRY CONFIRMED? ☐ YES ☐ NO

RACE NUMBER: _____

START TIME / SIGN ON: _____

RESULT
POSITION: _____ TIME: _____ PACE: _____

KEY EVENT RACE DETAILS

EVENT: _____

DATE: _____

LOCATION: _____

ORGANISATION: _____

CONTACT: _____

PHONE: _____

ADDRESS: _____

WEBSITE: _____

EMAIL / SOCIAL: _____

ENTRY CONFIRMED? ☐ YES ☐ NO

RACE NUMBER: _____

START TIME / SIGN ON: _____

RESULT

POSITION: _____ TIME: _____ PACE: _____

KEY EVENT RACE DETAILS

EVENT: _____

DATE: _____

LOCATION: _____

ORGANISATION: _____

CONTACT: _____

PHONE: _____

ADDRESS: _____

WEBSITE: _____

EMAIL / SOCIAL: _____

ENTRY CONFIRMED? ☐ YES ☐ NO

RACE NUMBER: _____

START TIME / SIGN ON: _____

RESULT
POSITION: _____ TIME: _____ PACE: _____

KEY EVENT RACE DETAILS

EVENT: _____

DATE: _____

LOCATION: _____

ORGANISATION: _____

CONTACT: _____

PHONE: _____

ADDRESS: _____

WEBSITE: _____

EMAIL / SOCIAL: _____

ENTRY CONFIRMED? ☐ YES ☐ NO

RACE NUMBER: _____

START TIME / SIGN ON: _____

RESULT
POSITION: _____ TIME: _____ PACE: _____

MY 12 WEEK PLAN

	MONDAY	TUESDAY	WEDNESDAY
WEEK 1			
WEEK 2			
WEEK 3			
WEEK 4			
WEEK 5			
WEEK 6			
WEEK 7			
WEEK 8			
WEEK 9			
WEEK 10			
WEEK 11			
WEEK 12			

THURSDAY	FRIDAY	SATURDAY	SUNDAY

WEEKLY RUNNING LOG

MONTH:

MONDAY:

TUESDAY:

WEDNESDAY:

THURSDAY:

FRIDAY:

SATURDAY:

SUNDAY:

WEEKLY TOTAL:

WEEKLY RUNNING LOG

MONTH:

MONDAY:

TUESDAY:

WEDNESDAY:

THURSDAY:

FRIDAY:

SATURDAY:

SUNDAY:

WEEKLY TOTAL:

WEEKLY RUNNING LOG

MONTH:

MONDAY:

TUESDAY:

WEDNESDAY:

THURSDAY:

FRIDAY:

SATURDAY:

SUNDAY:

WEEKLY TOTAL:

WEEKLY RUNNING LOG

MONTH:

MONDAY:

TUESDAY:

WEDNESDAY:

THURSDAY:

FRIDAY:

SATURDAY:

SUNDAY:

WEEKLY TOTAL:

MONTH END REVIEW

MONTH:

TOTAL DISTANCE:

TOTAL TIME:

AVG. PACE:

PERSONAL MONTHLY CHECK-IN

THE PAST MONTH'S RUNNING WAS:_____

MY PHYSICAL CONDITION WAS: _____

MY MENTAL CONDITION WAS: _____

THE POSITIVES WERE: _____

THE NEGATIVES WERE: _____

THINGS I'VE LEARNT: _____

RUNNING HIGHLIGHT OF THE MONTH WAS: _____

_____

_____

_____

WHAT I'LL APPLY TO NEXT MONTH'S RUNNING:_____

_____

_____

WEEKLY RUNNING LOG

MONTH:

MONDAY:

TUESDAY:

WEDNESDAY:

THURSDAY:

FRIDAY:

SATURDAY:

SUNDAY:

WEEKLY TOTAL:

WEEKLY RUNNING LOG

MONTH:

MONDAY:

TUESDAY:

WEDNESDAY:

THURSDAY:

FRIDAY:

SATURDAY:

SUNDAY:

WEEKLY TOTAL:

WEEKLY RUNNING LOG

MONTH:

MONDAY:

TUESDAY:

WEDNESDAY:

THURSDAY:

FRIDAY:

SATURDAY:

SUNDAY:

WEEKLY TOTAL:

WEEKLY RUNNING LOG

MONTH:

MONDAY:

TUESDAY:

WEDNESDAY:

THURSDAY:

FRIDAY:

SATURDAY:

SUNDAY:

WEEKLY TOTAL:

MONTH END REVIEW

MONTH:

_____

TOTAL DISTANCE:

_____

TOTAL TIME:

_____

AVG. PACE:

_____

PERSONAL MONTHLY CHECK-IN

THE PAST MONTH'S RUNNING WAS:_____

MY PHYSICAL CONDITION WAS: _____

MY MENTAL CONDITION WAS: _____

THE POSITIVES WERE: _____

THE NEGATIVES WERE: _____

THINGS I'VE LEARNT: _____

RUNNING HIGHLIGHT OF THE MONTH WAS: _____

_____

_____

_____

WHAT I'LL APPLY TO NEXT MONTH'S RUNNING:_____

_____

_____

WEEKLY RUNNING LOG

MONTH:

MONDAY:

TUESDAY:

WEDNESDAY:

THURSDAY:

FRIDAY:

SATURDAY:

SUNDAY:

WEEKLY TOTAL:

WEEKLY RUNNING LOG

MONTH:

MONDAY:

TUESDAY:

WEDNESDAY:

THURSDAY:

FRIDAY:

SATURDAY:

SUNDAY:

WEEKLY TOTAL:

WEEKLY RUNNING LOG

MONTH:

MONDAY:

TUESDAY:

WEDNESDAY:

THURSDAY:

FRIDAY:

SATURDAY:

SUNDAY:

WEEKLY TOTAL:

WEEKLY RUNNING LOG

MONTH:

MONDAY:

TUESDAY:

WEDNESDAY:

THURSDAY:

FRIDAY:

SATURDAY:

SUNDAY:

WEEKLY TOTAL:

MONTH END REVIEW

MONTH:

_____

TOTAL DISTANCE:

_____

TOTAL TIME:

_____

AVG. PACE:

_____

PERSONAL MONTHLY CHECK-IN

THE PAST MONTH'S RUNNING WAS: _____

MY PHYSICAL CONDITION WAS: _____

MY MENTAL CONDITION WAS: _____

THE POSITIVES WERE: _____

THE NEGATIVES WERE: _____

THINGS I'VE LEARNT: _____

RUNNING HIGHLIGHT OF THE MONTH WAS: _____

_____

_____

_____

WHAT I'LL APPLY TO NEXT MONTH'S RUNNING: _____

_____

_____

MY 12 WEEK PLAN

	MONDAY	TUESDAY	WEDNESDAY
WEEK 1			
WEEK 2			
WEEK 3			
WEEK 4			
WEEK 5			
WEEK 6			
WEEK 7			
WEEK 8			
WEEK 9			
WEEK 10			
WEEK 11			
WEEK 12			

THURSDAY	FRIDAY	SATURDAY	SUNDAY

WEEKLY RUNNING LOG

MONTH:

MONDAY:

TUESDAY:

WEDNESDAY:

THURSDAY:

FRIDAY:

SATURDAY:

SUNDAY:

WEEKLY TOTAL:

WEEKLY RUNNING LOG

MONTH:

MONDAY:

TUESDAY:

WEDNESDAY:

THURSDAY:

FRIDAY:

SATURDAY:

SUNDAY:

WEEKLY TOTAL:

WEEKLY RUNNING LOG

MONTH:

MONDAY:

TUESDAY:

WEDNESDAY:

THURSDAY:

FRIDAY:

SATURDAY:

SUNDAY:

WEEKLY TOTAL:

WEEKLY RUNNING LOG

MONTH:

MONDAY:

TUESDAY:

WEDNESDAY:

THURSDAY:

FRIDAY:

SATURDAY:

SUNDAY:

WEEKLY TOTAL:

MONTH END REVIEW

MONTH:

_____

TOTAL DISTANCE:

_____

TOTAL TIME:

_____

AVG. PACE:

_____

PERSONAL MONTHLY CHECK-IN

THE PAST MONTH'S RUNNING WAS:_____

MY PHYSICAL CONDITION WAS: _____

MY MENTAL CONDITION WAS: _____

THE POSITIVES WERE: _____

THE NEGATIVES WERE: _____

THINGS I'VE LEARNT: _____

RUNNING HIGHLIGHT OF THE MONTH WAS:_____

_____

_____

_____

WHAT I'LL APPLY TO NEXT MONTH'S RUNNING:_____

_____

_____

WEEKLY RUNNING LOG

MONTH:

MONDAY:

TUESDAY:

WEDNESDAY:

THURSDAY:

FRIDAY:

SATURDAY:

SUNDAY:

WEEKLY TOTAL:

WEEKLY RUNNING LOG

MONTH:

MONDAY:

TUESDAY:

WEDNESDAY:

THURSDAY:

FRIDAY:

SATURDAY:

SUNDAY:

WEEKLY TOTAL:

WEEKLY RUNNING LOG

MONTH:

MONDAY:

TUESDAY:

WEDNESDAY:

THURSDAY:

FRIDAY:

SATURDAY:

SUNDAY:

WEEKLY TOTAL:

WEEKLY RUNNING LOG

MONTH:

MONDAY:

TUESDAY:

WEDNESDAY:

THURSDAY:

FRIDAY:

SATURDAY:

SUNDAY:

WEEKLY TOTAL:

MONTH END REVIEW

MONTH:

TOTAL DISTANCE:

TOTAL TIME:

AVG. PACE:

PERSONAL MONTHLY CHECK-IN

THE PAST MONTH'S RUNNING WAS:_____

MY PHYSICAL CONDITION WAS:_____

MY MENTAL CONDITION WAS:_____

THE POSITIVES WERE:_____

THE NEGATIVES WERE:_____

THINGS I'VE LEARNT:_____

RUNNING HIGHLIGHT OF THE MONTH WAS:_____

_____

_____

_____

WHAT I'LL APPLY TO NEXT MONTH'S RUNNING:_____

_____

_____

WEEKLY RUNNING LOG

MONTH:

MONDAY:

TUESDAY:

WEDNESDAY:

THURSDAY:

FRIDAY:

SATURDAY:

SUNDAY:

WEEKLY TOTAL:

WEEKLY RUNNING LOG

MONTH:

MONDAY:

TUESDAY:

WEDNESDAY:

THURSDAY:

FRIDAY:

SATURDAY:

SUNDAY:

WEEKLY TOTAL:

WEEKLY RUNNING LOG

MONTH:

MONDAY:

TUESDAY:

WEDNESDAY:

THURSDAY:

FRIDAY:

SATURDAY:

SUNDAY:

WEEKLY TOTAL:

WEEKLY RUNNING LOG

MONTH:

MONDAY:

TUESDAY:

WEDNESDAY:

THURSDAY:

FRIDAY:

SATURDAY:

SUNDAY:

WEEKLY TOTAL:

MONTH END REVIEW

MONTH:

_____

TOTAL DISTANCE:

_____

TOTAL TIME:

_____

AVG. PACE:

_____

PERSONAL MONTHLY CHECK-IN

THE PAST MONTH'S RUNNING WAS: _____

MY PHYSICAL CONDITION WAS: _____

MY MENTAL CONDITION WAS: _____

THE POSITIVES WERE: _____

THE NEGATIVES WERE: _____

THINGS I'VE LEARNT: _____

RUNNING HIGHLIGHT OF THE MONTH WAS: _____

_____

_____

_____

WHAT I'LL APPLY TO NEXT MONTH'S RUNNING: _____

_____

_____

MY 12 WEEK PLAN

	MONDAY	TUESDAY	WEDNESDAY
WEEK 1			
WEEK 2			
WEEK 3			
WEEK 4			
WEEK 5			
WEEK 6			
WEEK 7			
WEEK 8			
WEEK 9			
WEEK 10			
WEEK 11			
WEEK 12			

THURSDAY	FRIDAY	SATURDAY	SUNDAY

WEEKLY RUNNING LOG

MONTH:

MONDAY:

TUESDAY:

WEDNESDAY:

THURSDAY:

FRIDAY:

SATURDAY:

SUNDAY:

WEEKLY TOTAL:

WEEKLY RUNNING LOG

MONTH:

MONDAY:

TUESDAY:

WEDNESDAY:

THURSDAY:

FRIDAY:

SATURDAY:

SUNDAY:

WEEKLY TOTAL:

WEEKLY RUNNING LOG

MONTH:

MONDAY:

TUESDAY:

WEDNESDAY:

THURSDAY:

FRIDAY:

SATURDAY:

SUNDAY:

WEEKLY TOTAL:

WEEKLY RUNNING LOG

MONTH:

MONDAY:

TUESDAY:

WEDNESDAY:

THURSDAY:

FRIDAY:

SATURDAY:

SUNDAY:

WEEKLY TOTAL:

MONTH END REVIEW

MONTH:

_____

TOTAL DISTANCE:

_____

TOTAL TIME:

_____

AVG. PACE:

_____

PERSONAL MONTHLY CHECK-IN

THE PAST MONTH'S RUNNING WAS: _____

MY PHYSICAL CONDITION WAS: _____

MY MENTAL CONDITION WAS: _____

THE POSITIVES WERE: _____

THE NEGATIVES WERE: _____

THINGS I'VE LEARNT: _____

RUNNING HIGHLIGHT OF THE MONTH WAS: _____

_____

_____

_____

WHAT I'LL APPLY TO NEXT MONTH'S RUNNING: _____

_____

_____

WEEKLY RUNNING LOG

MONTH:

MONDAY:

TUESDAY:

WEDNESDAY:

THURSDAY:

FRIDAY:

SATURDAY:

SUNDAY:

WEEKLY TOTAL:

WEEKLY RUNNING LOG

MONTH:

MONDAY:

TUESDAY:

WEDNESDAY:

THURSDAY:

FRIDAY:

SATURDAY:

SUNDAY:

WEEKLY TOTAL:

WEEKLY RUNNING LOG

MONTH:

MONDAY:

TUESDAY:

WEDNESDAY:

THURSDAY:

FRIDAY:

SATURDAY:

SUNDAY:

WEEKLY TOTAL:

WEEKLY RUNNING LOG

MONTH:

MONDAY:

TUESDAY:

WEDNESDAY:

THURSDAY:

FRIDAY:

SATURDAY:

SUNDAY:

WEEKLY TOTAL:

MONTH END REVIEW

MONTH:

_____

TOTAL DISTANCE:

_____

TOTAL TIME:

_____

AVG. PACE:

_____

PERSONAL MONTHLY CHECK-IN

THE PAST MONTH'S RUNNING WAS:_____

MY PHYSICAL CONDITION WAS:_____

MY MENTAL CONDITION WAS:_____

THE POSITIVES WERE:_____

THE NEGATIVES WERE:_____

THINGS I'VE LEARNT:_____

RUNNING HIGHLIGHT OF THE MONTH WAS:_____

_____

_____

_____

WHAT I'LL APPLY TO NEXT MONTH'S RUNNING:_____

_____

_____

WEEKLY RUNNING LOG

MONTH:

MONDAY:

TUESDAY:

WEDNESDAY:

THURSDAY:

FRIDAY:

SATURDAY:

SUNDAY:

WEEKLY TOTAL:

WEEKLY RUNNING LOG

MONTH:

MONDAY:

TUESDAY:

WEDNESDAY:

THURSDAY:

FRIDAY:

SATURDAY:

SUNDAY:

WEEKLY TOTAL:

WEEKLY RUNNING LOG

MONTH:

MONDAY:

TUESDAY:

WEDNESDAY:

THURSDAY:

FRIDAY:

SATURDAY:

SUNDAY:

WEEKLY TOTAL:

WEEKLY RUNNING LOG

MONTH:

MONDAY:

TUESDAY:

WEDNESDAY:

THURSDAY:

FRIDAY:

SATURDAY:

SUNDAY:

WEEKLY TOTAL:

MONTH END REVIEW

MONTH:

_____

TOTAL DISTANCE:

_____

TOTAL TIME:

_____

AVG. PACE:

_____

PERSONAL MONTHLY CHECK-IN

THE PAST MONTH'S RUNNING WAS:_____

MY PHYSICAL CONDITION WAS: _____

MY MENTAL CONDITION WAS: _____

THE POSITIVES WERE: _____

THE NEGATIVES WERE: _____

THINGS I'VE LEARNT: _____

RUNNING HIGHLIGHT OF THE MONTH WAS: _____

_____

_____

_____

WHAT I'LL APPLY TO NEXT MONTH'S RUNNING:_____

_____

_____

TRAINING & HEALTH CONTACTS

CONTACT NAME: _____

DISCIPLINE: _____

PHONE: _____

ADDRESS: _____

_____

EMAIL / SOCIAL: _____

CONTACT NAME: _____

DISCIPLINE: _____

PHONE: _____

ADDRESS: _____

_____

EMAIL / SOCIAL: _____

COACHES, PERSONAL TRAINERS, DOCTORS, PHYSIOTHERAPISTS, CHIROPRACTORS & OSTEOPATHS

CONTACT NAME:

DISCIPLINE:

PHONE:

ADDRESS:

EMAIL / SOCIAL:

CONTACT NAME:

DISCIPLINE:

PHONE:

ADDRESS:

EMAIL / SOCIAL:

CONTACT NAME: _____

DISCIPLINE: _____

PHONE: _____

ADDRESS: _____

_____

EMAIL / SOCIAL: _____

CONTACT NAME: _____

DISCIPLINE: _____

PHONE: _____

ADDRESS: _____

_____

EMAIL / SOCIAL: _____

CONTACT NAME: _____

DISCIPLINE: _____

PHONE: _____

ADDRESS: _____

_____

EMAIL / SOCIAL: _____

CONTACT NAME: _____

DISCIPLINE: _____

PHONE: _____

ADDRESS: _____

_____

EMAIL / SOCIAL: _____

CONTACT NAME: _____

DISCIPLINE: _____

PHONE: _____

ADDRESS: _____

_____

EMAIL / SOCIAL: _____

CONTACT NAME: _____

DISCIPLINE: _____

PHONE: _____

ADDRESS: _____

_____

EMAIL / SOCIAL: _____

CONTACT NAME: _____

DISCIPLINE: _____

PHONE: _____

ADDRESS: _____

_____

EMAIL / SOCIAL: _____

CONTACT NAME: _____

DISCIPLINE: _____

PHONE: _____

ADDRESS: _____

_____

EMAIL / SOCIAL: _____

CONTACT NAME: _____

DISCIPLINE: _____

PHONE: _____

ADDRESS: _____

_____

EMAIL / SOCIAL: _____

CONTACT NAME: _____

DISCIPLINE: _____

PHONE: _____

ADDRESS: _____

_____

EMAIL / SOCIAL: _____

CONTACT NAME: _____

DISCIPLINE: _____

PHONE: _____

ADDRESS: _____

_____

EMAIL / SOCIAL: _____

CONTACT NAME: _____

DISCIPLINE: _____

PHONE: _____

ADDRESS: _____

_____

EMAIL / SOCIAL: _____

RECOVERY & RELAXATION

RECOVERY & RELAXATION

RECOVERY & RELAXATION

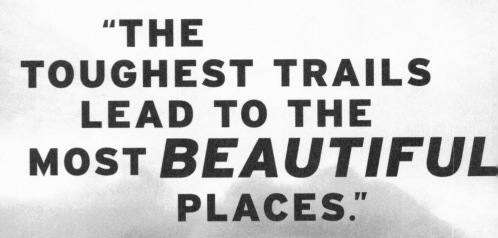

"THE TOUGHEST TRAILS LEAD TO THE MOST *BEAUTIFUL* PLACES."